Essential Food Hygiene

Dr. R.J. Donaldson OBE

SECOND EDITION

First published in 1988 by The Royal Society of Health,
RSH House, 38A St George's Drive, London SW1V 4BH.
Telephone: 0171-630 0121

First edition: 200,000 copies
Second edition 1993

ISBN 0-901619-11-6

Printed by Hartley Reproductions Ltd. of Dartford, Kent
Telephone 01322 287676

ACKNOWLEDGEMENTS

Janet Strangeways and Yvonne Young kindly and willingly contributed their specialist knowledge to sections of the text.

Suggestions from Sylvia McEwan and Dalma Marossey have been included in the text.

Graham King is to be congratulated for his skill and enterprise in controlling costs without affecting the quality of this book.

Chris and Kathy Turrall provided me with an insight into the arcane world of book design and Barry Teversham's helpful assistance made light the printing problems.

It was my great good fortune, as I commenced re-writing the book, that Bob Campbell agreed to act as my research assistant. His dedicated work in collecting and collating information combined with his drafting skills proved an invaluable asset. It would also be remiss not to record my best thanks to Bob's wife, Jean, who entered the entire text on her word-processor thus making my task of re-writing much easier.

INTRODUCTION

The many changes that have occurred since
Essential Food Hygiene was first published in 1988
are reflected in this Second Edition which contains
much new material and takes account of recent
changes in food safety legislation.

But the main message is unchanged: food-related
illnesses can be prevented.

Understanding how these illnesses are caused and
how they can be avoided is the challenge facing all
those involved in the various stages of preparing
food for human consumption. **Knowledge is the key.**

Fortunately, there is now a far greater appreciation
of the role that training can play in making food safe
for consumption. Each year around 100,000 food
handlers gain the Royal Society of Health Certificate
in Essential Food Hygiene—the examination
associated with this book.

It is hoped that this new edition will make a
contribution—albeit modest given the scale of the
task—towards higher standards of food hygiene
wherever food is processed, stored, prepared, served
or sold.

The aim of the Author is to take readers easily and
directly to the heart of the subject.

CONTENTS

1
2
3
4
5
6
7
8
9
10
11

A HISTORICAL NOTE

1 ▶ **This Section briefly outlines the history of our current understanding of food poisoning and points out that in spite of modern scientific knowledge many mistakes are made.**

EARLY TIMES

Concern about what food is edible and what food is not, has its origins in ancient times. The Old Testament of The Bible contains laws laid down by Moses not only about which animals were fit for human consumption but also about cleanliness in general. Much of this was based on practical knowledge. Food poisoning as a disease entity has been recognised for centuries.

BACTERIA THE KEY

However, it was only about 100 years ago that the scientific basis as to the cause of communicable diseases, including food poisoning, became known when the famous French chemist, Pasteur, demonstrated that bacteria could cause disease. At about the same time, the German physician Robert Koch recognised that bacteria were responsible for a number of diseases, including cholera.

The dawning of this scientific era required a public education programme to dispel the myths and misconceptions, and also to persuade reluctant government bodies to take action.

In these campaigns the Royal Society of Health took a leading role to promote health and improve the social conditions of the times. It was formed in 1876, and six years later Queen Victoria—who displayed great interest in the health of her people— became its patron.

For centuries there have been accounts of people becoming ill after eating food. This was thought to be due to chemical poisons—sometimes added deliberately. Later, a chemical substance called ptomaine, which is formed in protein-food during putrification, was implicated. Eventually, when ptomaine was extracted from food it was found to be harmless when taken by mouth.

THE LINK

The definitive link with bacteria as a cause of food poisoning came in 1888. A German doctor named Gaertner isolated bacteria from the organs of a man who had died in a food poisoning outbreak. He found identical bacteria in the left-over meat that the man and his companions had consumed as well as in the carcass from which the meat had come. Thus the cause was established. It was also gradually realised that food could be heavily contaminated with bacteria and yet smell and taste the same as normal food.

By the beginning of this century food had become more plentiful and cheap and the small eating houses of the day were often very insanitary. Paradoxically, there were few reports of food poisoning outbreaks, possibly because of the small number of people involved. However, the more likely explanation is that the meat was cooked and served immediately to the customers, unlike the mass catering of today when food is cooked and sometimes held, unfortunately, at the temperature at which bacteria can grow.

A CAUTIONARY TALE

During the last 100 years more groups of bacteria have been implicated in food poisoning and new types have been imported.

For example, during World War Two, when Britain was very dependent upon imported food, dried-egg from the U.S.A. was popular. Some of this dried-egg contained small numbers of food poisoning bacteria. The illness was caused by the method of preparation and cooking. What often happened was that the housewife would make the mixture of dried-egg and milk the night before, leave it in the warm kitchen and next morning cook it quickly and lightly for her husband going to work the early shift. Hence the bacteria were provided with the nutrients, moisture, warmth, and time to grow profusely, and the cooking process was inadequate to destroy them all. Thus new members of the families of food poisoning bacteria were introduced into war-time Britain.

Unfortunately many of the outbreaks of food poisoning today still relate to similar mistakes, when the "high risk" foods are held for too long within the "Temperature Danger Zone". These problems are discussed in more detail later.

FOOD POISONING

This Section defines food hygiene and food poisoning, and provides the profoundly depressing facts about the increasing number of reported food poisoning cases.

FOOD HYGIENE is the action taken to ensure that food is handled, stored, prepared and served in such a way, and under such conditions, as to prevent—as far as possible—the contamination of food.

FOOD POISONING can be broadly defined as those conditions caused by the ingestion of contaminated food or drink in which the main symptoms are usually diarrhoea and vomiting, singularly or together, often accompanied by nausea ("feeling sick") and stomach pains.

The modern definition of food poisoning includes, in addition, food and water borne illnesses which have different symptoms.

Food poisoning is weakening and extremely unpleasant, even to healthy people. However, **infants, pregnant women, old people and those having weakened immunity** (known as the "at risk" groups) can become seriously ill and may even die.

The onset of symptoms is usually sudden and may start within 2 hours of taking the food but there may be an interval of several days. The illness typically lasts 1 or 2 days but sometimes can continue for a week or more.

THE INCIDENCE OF FOOD POISONING

Food poisoning strikes thousands of people every year, the total number of new cases being called the **incidence** of food poisoning.

In 1991 there were approximately 86,000 known cases of food-related illness in England and Wales. These figures represent only the tip of the iceberg because many cases are not reported. An independent survey has suggested that **8 million** working days are lost each year in the United Kingdom because of food poisoning.

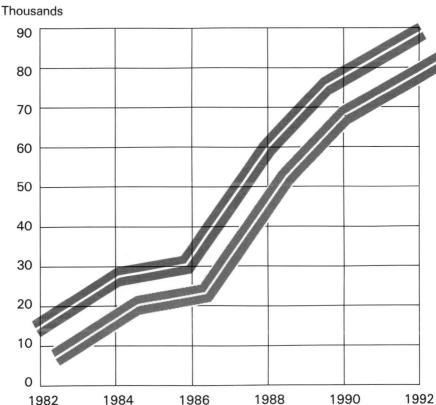

CASES OF FOOD POISONING IN ENGLAND AND WALES

Thousands

This is all profoundly depressing particularly as the incidence of food poisoning has been on an upward trend for many years. Many other countries are having the same experience.

There is no single reason for the increase but some contributory factors have been identified:

- more intensive methods of rearing animals
- contaminated animal feed
- much food is cooked or partly cooked before it reaches the consumer and, as it proceeds along the distributive chain, there may be breakdowns in the strict temperature and general hygiene controls required to keep the food in prime condition
- preservatives play an important role in protecting food against bacterial contamination but these are now being used less because of consumer fears that they can cause serious diseases
- people used to buy food daily and cook it at home shortly after purchase. Nowadays they buy in bulk—particularly chilled foods—without always being aware of the proper way to store and prepare the food
- people now eat more poultry, a food prone to bacterial contamination
- there is now far more eating out than formerly. Poor standards in the household kitchen have consequences only for the family but in a catering establishment they can cause illness to a very large number of people.

There is general agreement that one of the main strategies for preventing food poisoning lies in the **better education** of all those involved with the various aspects of food handling from the farm to the table.

A 1990 survey showed standards of hygiene to be unsatisfactory in as many as one in eight of the food premises surveyed. Take-away outlets, cafés, restaurants and food manufacturers were identified as posing the highest health risk.

The survey concluded that the main factors contributing to health risks were:

- ineffective monitoring of temperatures
- poor staff hygiene awareness
- cross-contamination resulting from poor practices
- inadequate hand-washing facilities
- lack of management hygiene awareness

CONTAMINATION OF FOOD

Food poisoning is caused by contaminated food. Food can be contaminated by:

- bacteria
- viruses
- other poisons

BACTERIA

Bacteria are small living organisms—a colony of 25,000 could be accommodated on the point of a needle. They are by far the most common cause of food poisoning in Britain. Later, we shall be discussing bacteria in more detail.

VIRUSES

Viruses are tiny particles—even smaller than bacteria—that can be identified only by using a special microscope. They grow only in living tissue, thus cannot grow in food. The part they play in causing food poisoning is not fully understood but they are implicated in other food-related illnesses such as Hepatitis A (infective jaundice). Although we shall not be considering viruses in detail, you should note that many of the measures that prevent contamination by bacteria also reduce the risk of viral infection.

OTHER POISONS

Occasionally, chemical poisons can accidentally get into food perhaps from weed killers and insecticides. Fruit sprayed with pesticides may also cause chemical food poisoning and this is why it is better to wash fruit and vegetables before they are eaten.

It is possible, also, for high acid foods such as tomatoes to act on the metal of a cooking vessel causing traces of the metal to enter the food.

Poisoning can also result from eating poisonous plants or fungi such as toadstools, poisonous berries or seeds.

These other poisons are infrequent causes of food poisoning and will not be discussed any further in this book which, as indicated earlier, is concerned with the **food poisoning bacteria.**

NOTE ON ALLERGIES

Some people may suffer symptoms as a result of eating certain foods simply because they happen to be sensitive to them—in the same way that hay fever sufferers are sensitive to pollen during the summer. This is called an allergic reaction: it is not the result of food being contaminated.

Shellfish, strawberries and cheese are examples of foods to which some people are allergic. Generally, people who have allergies become aware of the foods they should avoid.

2

BACTERIA

This Section describes bacteria as small living creatures that require food, moisture, warmth and time to grow.

THE NATURE OF BACTERIA

Bacteria are tiny living creatures often known as "germs". They are so small that it is impossible to see them without a microscope. Bacteria are usually round or rod shaped.

Bacteria are everywhere in soil, dust and water, in the air around us, and on our bodies

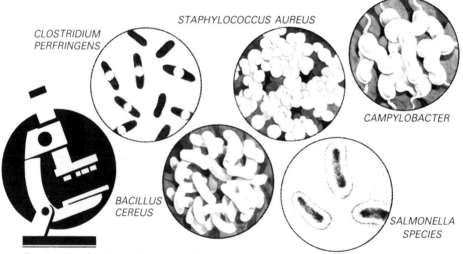

CLOSTRIDIUM PERFRINGENS

STAPHYLOCOCCUS AUREUS

CAMPYLOBACTER

BACILLUS CEREUS

SALMONELLA SPECIES

Food poisoning bacteria as seen through a microscope

Most bacteria are harmless and some are even beneficial to man like those in our gut (intestines) that aid digestion.

Another family of bacteria can cause food to smell, to lose texture and flavour, and generally to decay. The food becomes so unpleasant that people will not eat it. These are referred to as food spoilage bacteria. They have an important role in nature by decomposing dead vegetable and animal matter and thus aiding the essential re-cycling process.

Some harmful bacteria found in food—often in relatively small numbers—can cause serious diseases such as typhoid fever. This, fortunately, is an uncommon occurrence in Britain today.

However our concern is with the food poisoning bacteria that can contaminate and multiply in foods if conditions are right for them.

SPORES

Some kinds of bacteria are capable of forming protective coverings called **spores**. This protection enables bacteria to remain alive, but inactive, in situations that normally would kill them. Later, if conditions become suitable, the spores change into the usual form of bacteria that then multiply rapidly.

Spores can withstand high cooking temperatures and are able to survive situations where nutrients or moisture are not immediately available.

HOW FOOD POISONING BACTERIA GROW

3

Bacteria are living things like ourselves and to live and grow must have the following FOUR conditions:

FOOD	MOISTURE	WARMTH	TIME

FOOD

Certain foods—most of which have a high protein content—are particularly rich in nutrients and contain moisture and therefore provide excellent conditions for bacterial growth if kept in warm conditions. These are known as the **"high risk foods"**.

High risk foods are implicated in at least 75% of all cases of food poisoning.

The main categories of high risk foods are:

● **cooked meat and poultry; cooked meat products; gravy, soup and stock**

These foods are particularly rich in the nutrients that bacteria need to grow. If kept under warm conditions even a small number of bacteria will become many millions in a short time.

● milk and eggs and products made from them

Milk and eggs, and foods containing milk and eggs such as cream, custard or mayonnaise are often involved in cases of food poisoning. Usually this is because they have been kept in warm conditions or have been contaminated by a food handler.

Certain types of cheese are also high risk.

● shellfish

Mussels, oysters, prawns, crabs or lobsters may eat food that is contaminated, or they may pick up food poisoning bacteria and viruses from polluted water. For example, shellfish such as oysters could have been taken from sewage polluted waters. The risk to humans is greatest if the shellfish are eaten raw, for example, oysters.

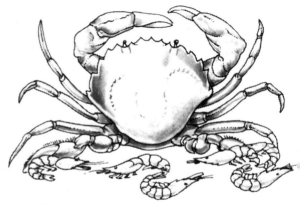

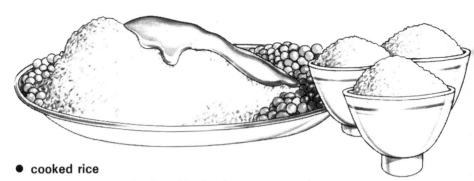

● cooked rice

Bacterial spores can be found in dry rice: once water is added to the rice during cooking the bacteria become active. Some of the bacteria may survive the cooking temperature. If, following cooking, the rice is not eaten immediately or not refrigerated, the bacteria will grow profusely and produce a toxin (poison) which may persist even if the rice is re-heated before being consumed.

Foods containing sugar, salt or acid—such as jam or pickles—discourage the growth of bacteria. Some foods have preservatives (chemical substances) added to them to restrict the growth of bacteria.

Bacterial growth may also be affected by the presence or absence of oxygen.

There is more information on how bacteria are affected by acid and oxygen in the Appendix.

MOISTURE

To grow, bacteria need moisture and this can be found in many foods including the high risk foods.

Bacteria are less likely to survive in dried food such as powdered milk or dried eggs but any bacteria that do survive under such dry conditions begin to grow again if fluids are added to the food. The story of dried eggs has already been mentioned in Section 1.

One of the reasons why sugar and salt discourage the growth of bacteria is that they take up the moisture that is then denied to the bacteria. Similarly, when food is frozen its moisture turns into ice and is not available to the bacteria.

WARMTH

The temperatures referred to throughout the book are in degrees Celsius (°C).

Bacteria that cause food poisoning will grow at temperatures between 5°C and 63°C; they grow most quickly at a temperature of around 37°C, which is the normal temperature of the human body.

For this reason, the range of temperatures between **5°C and 63°C** is known as the

TEMPERATURE DANGER ZONE

Even a small number of bacteria can grow rapidly in food that is allowed to remain in the Temperature Danger Zone.

Temperatures outside the Danger Zone are less suitable for bacteria. Although bacteria thrive in warmth they are usually killed by **heat**. Most bacteria are killed by a temperature of **at least 70°C** providing this is reached at the centre of the food and is held **for a sufficient time.**

However, some bacteria and their toxins (poisons) require higher temperatures for a longer period of time before they are destroyed.

Pasteurisation is a method of destroying bacteria by rapidly heating the food to a sufficiently high temperature. Milk, liquid egg, ice cream and certain canned foods are examples of food treated in this way.

In **cold** conditions, that is below 5°C, bacteria do not grow or grow only very slowly. At very low temperatures some will die, but many will survive and grow again if warm conditions return.

TIME

3

Given moist, warm food, bacteria simply need **time** to grow. It is often carelessness that allows them the time they need, such as when food is allowed to remain in the Temperature Danger Zone.

Each bacterial cell multiplies by splitting itself into two so that **1** bacterial cell becomes **2** bacterial cells. Each of these **2** bacteria then split to make **4** bacteria. Each of the **4** bacteria split into two again, making **8** bacteria, and so on. Binary fission is the term used to describe this process of splitting and multiplying.

If the temperature is suitable, bacteria will reproduce in this way every 10 – 20 minutes, indeed some take even less time.

This means that after reproducing at around this rate for only 4 or 5 hours, **one bacterium** will have multiplied to **many thousands.** In practice, the size of the infection will be even greater because contaminated food usually carries considerably more than one bacterium at the outset.

KEEP HIGH RISK FOODS
ABOVE 63°C OR BELOW 5°C

FOOD

MOISTURE

WARMTH

TIME

IF THESE FOUR CONDITIONS COME
TOGETHER BACTERIA WILL MULTIPLY RAPIDLY

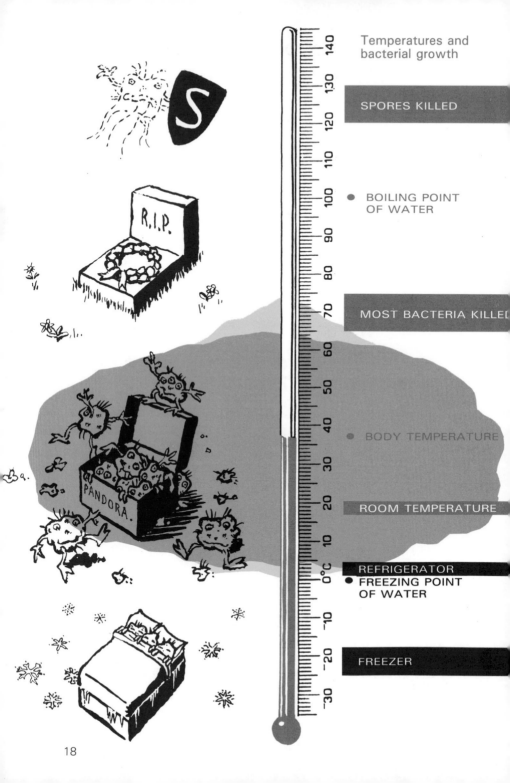

Temperatures and
bacterial growth

140
SPORES KILLED
130
120
110
● BOILING POINT
OF WATER
100
90
80
70
MOST BACTERIA KILLED
60
50
40
● BODY TEMPERATURE
30
20
ROOM TEMPERATURE
10
0°C
REFRIGERATOR
● FREEZING POINT
OF WATER
-10
-20
FREEZER
-30

HOW BACTERIA CAUSE FOOD POISONING

This Section explains the way bacteria act to produce symptoms of food poisoning and gives the main sources of these bacteria.

BACTERIA AND FOOD POISONING

A large number of bacteria are needed to produce symptoms, so they require time and the right conditions to grow. There are a number of different kinds of food poisoning bacteria, each having its own name. **Salmonella** is the name given to the family of bacteria that is responsible for a large proportion of the reported food poisoning outbreaks in Britain.

4

(The term Salmonella comes from the name of the American vet—Dr. Salmon—who in 1885 was the first to isolate this family of bacteria.)

Bacteria cause food poisoning in different ways, their behaviour depending on the particular type of bacteria. Their various names tend to be long and often difficult to pronounce but there is no need for you to remember the individual names. If, however, you wish to know more about them you can read the information at the Appendix.

Bacteria can act to cause food poisoning in one of three ways:

● bacteria that grow throughout the food in large numbers, so that when we eat the food we eat the bacteria too.

*For example, a number of **Salmonella** bacteria could be transferred by slicing cold roast beef with an unwashed knife previously used for cutting up a raw chicken. If given sufficient time within the Temperature Danger Zone, many millions of bacteria will grow.*

● bacteria that are difficult to kill with heat.

*A good example of this is a bacterium with the long name **Clostridium perfringens,** which is often found in raw meat and poultry. It has the capacity to change into a resistant form called spores. Some of these spores can survive the normal cooking process. A joint of meat in which even a few spores have survived cooking, if left to **cool slowly** in a warm kitchen, can result in the spores changing back into the usual form of bacteria which then grow very rapidly.*

19

- bacteria that release their toxins (poison) into the food before the food is eaten.

*One such bacterium is called **Staphylococcus aureus** (found in our nose, throat and wounds) which can produce poisons in custards and trifles as well as in cooked meat and poultry . . . if allowed time to grow in warm conditions.*

Food poisoning bacteria are invisible to the naked eye and do not usually cause any change to the appearance, smell or taste of food. Individuals cannot therefore rely on any of their senses to tell them whether or not food is contaminated. This means that food handlers must practise very high standards of food hygiene to ensure that food does not become contaminated.

4

SOURCES OF FOOD POISONING BACTERIA

Before you can protect food from bacteria you need to know where the bacteria come from and how they come to be present in the food we eat. Most come from animal and human sources.

RAW FOODS

Many bacteria, including two of those we have just discussed—Salmonella and Clostridium perfringens—live in the intestines, or "gut", of animals. The animals concerned usually have no symptoms, and just carry the bacteria. Thus bacteria can be transferred to meat intended for human consumption.

For this reason, it is wise to think of all raw meat and poultry, as well as the juices that come from them, as already carrying many food poisoning bacteria before they arrive in the food area. Raw meat and particularly raw poultry are frequent sources of food poisoning outbreaks.

Other raw foods that may carry food poisoning bacteria are eggs—both inside and on the shell—and seafood such as oysters and mussels. Rice can also be contaminated. Unpasteurised milk (little is now sold) may harbour dangerous bacteria.

In fact, many raw foods, including those used in salads, are naturally contaminated by bacteria but the ones mentioned pose the greatest risk.

SOURCES OF FOOD POISONING BACTERIA

MICE
AND RATS

FLIES

RAW MEAT, POULTRY AND EGGS

COCKROACHES

SHELLFISH

BIRDS

4

WASTE FOOD AND DIRT

HUMAN HANDLERS

WAYS IN WHICH STAPHYLOCOCCUS AUREUS ENTERS FOOD

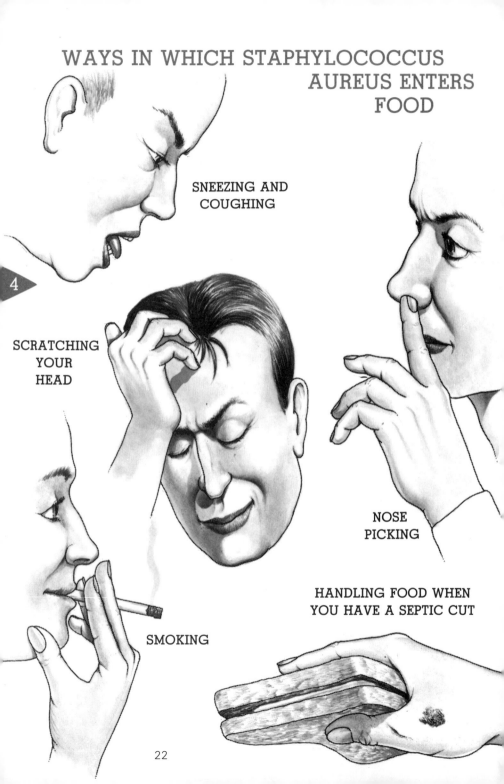

4

SNEEZING AND
COUGHING

SCRATCHING
YOUR
HEAD

NOSE
PICKING

SMOKING

HANDLING FOOD WHEN
YOU HAVE A SEPTIC CUT

THE HUMAN BODY

Bacteria that can cause food poisoning are carried in several areas of your own body—for example, the previously noted Staphylococcus aureus, found on your hands and skin, in your nose, throat, mouth, ears, hair and fingernails. Bacteria that cause food poisoning, such as Salmonella, can also be present in our intestines, and thus in faeces (stools).

People infected with food poisoning bacteria often have no symptoms and are referred to as "carriers" because, although not feeling ill themselves, they can transfer the infection to foods with their hands unless they are scrupulous in their personal hygiene.

Careless food handling is one of the causes of bacterial contamination—with bacteria being transferred from hands, mouth and nose or from cuts, grazes, scratches or boils.

4

A WAY IN WHICH SALMONELLA GETS INTO FOOD

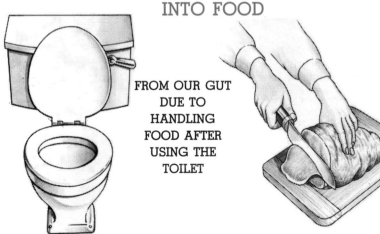

FROM OUR GUT
DUE TO
HANDLING
FOOD AFTER
USING THE
TOILET

OTHER SOURCES WITHIN THE ENVIRONMENT

Pests—flies and other insects, birds, rats and mice, carry bacteria on their bodies and in their urine and droppings. They can infect food or places where food may be placed.

Pets,too, carry bacteria on and in their bodies and should not be allowed into food areas.

Waste food and **rubbish** provide ideal conditions in which bacteria can live and reproduce because they are warm and are left undisturbed for several hours.

HYGIENE CONTROL

This Section gives details of action you should take to prevent food becoming contaminated.

CONTAMINATION

Hygiene control is the adoption of practices which will reduce the risk of clean food becoming contaminated. The aim of hygiene control is to *prevent the spread* of bacteria.

Clean food can be contaminated:

- through contact with contaminated foods, particularly raw meat and poultry
- through contact with work-surfaces and equipment
- by the food handler
- by pests and waste

The transfer of bacteria from a contaminated food to an uncontaminated (clean) food is called **cross-contamination.**

FOOD-TO-FOOD CONTAMINATION

Always assume that raw meat and especially raw poultry are heavily infected with bacteria when brought into the food area. So keep raw meat and poultry—including their juices—well away from other foods but particularly from cooked meat and cooked poultry.

Many other raw foods carry bacteria that will infect clean foods if they come into contact. Take special care with **shellfish, eggs,** and **soil from vegetables.** And remember that bacteria on the *shell* of an egg can be transferred to the inside if the shell is not broken carefully.

To prevent cross-contamination from raw foods you should:

■ identify separate parts of the work area for dealing with

raw meat or poultry
and
foods that will be eaten without being subjected to any further treatment (e.g. cooking) that would destroy any bacteria that might get on to them

■ keep other raw foods away from foods that could become similarly contaminated

■ use different refrigerators for storing raw and cooked foods but, if only one refrigerator is available, keep the raw foods on the lower shelves and the other foods above them.

5

EQUIPMENT-TO-FOOD CONTAMINATION

Equipment and work-surfaces can easily become contaminated by **foods** particularly raw meat and poultry, by **pests** and even by the **food handler.** Then the contaminated surface or equipment will pass on the bacteria to food with which it comes into contact.

Treat as contaminated any items that have come into contact with raw meat and poultry or their juices—work-surfaces, chopping boards, utensils, trays and equipment such as mincers, slicers and knives. These items often retain minute particles of raw food that can harbour bacteria.

Equipment and work-surfaces must be cleaned immediately after use. Otherwise, there is a risk of someone else using them without realising they might be contaminated.

Remember, too, that work-surfaces and equipment that *look* clean may have become contaminated by insects or even humans but you cannot tell simply by looking. You will never see the bacteria but they can be there!

You must:

- thoroughly and immediately clean work-surfaces where raw meat and poultry have been handled

- keep utensils and equipment used in the preparation of raw meats and poultry separate from those used for other foods

- maintain a high standard of general cleanliness of worktops and equipment

COLOUR CODING

Separation of utensils and equipment can be achieved through **colour coding.** Under colour coding, items of equipment such as knives, chopping boards and wiping cloths are given different coloured tags to show when and where they should be used.

EXAMPLES OF COLOUR CODING

TAG	Knives, chopping boards, cloths etc. to be used only for
RED	Raw meat and poultry
BLUE	Fish
BROWN	Cooked meats
GREEN	Vegetables and fruit
WHITE	General purpose/bakery

WIPING CLOTHS

Wiping cloths pick up bacteria when used to clean worktops, trays, display units and equipment. Once on a cloth, the bacteria can easily be transferred to other parts of the food area. There is a special danger if the cloth is used for wiping areas where raw meat and poultry have been lying and is then used somewhere else.

So, although we think of wiping cloths as a means of keeping things clean they can just as easily become a means of *spreading* bacteria.

Always:

- keep separate wiping cloths for use with the different kinds of food

- keep wiping cloths used in raw food areas out of other food areas

- use disposable wiping cloths, if available

- work with clean cloths—boil cloths frequently

FOOD HANDLER-TO-FOOD CONTAMINATION

To reduce the risk of your contaminating food:

- use tongs, plastic gloves, food bags or food wrapping paper to pick up items of food

- carry food in containers, or on trays or plates

- avoid touching parts of dishes and cutlery that will come into contact with food

- never use your fingers to test food

- use cutlery only once for tasting food—then wash it thoroughly before re-use

- do not lick your fingers to separate wrapping paper

- do not blow into paper bags to open them

The important subject of **personal hygiene** is dealt with in the next Section.

5

OTHER WAYS OF CONTAMINATING FOOD

Prepared food should be kept under refrigeration or in storage units and removed only a short time before being required for consumption. But even in this short ''stand out'' time there can be contamination by **pests,** particularly flies, and from bacteria in **waste food** or in the atmosphere generally.

If you cannot avoid standing out prepared food:

■ place it in the coolest part of the food room

■ keep it covered

■ keep it away from a window or waste bin

■ do not place the food where cleaning is taking place

PERSONAL HYGIENE

This Section explains why strict standards of personal hygiene are necessary and how these can be achieved.

PERSONAL RESPONSIBILITIES

Bacteria live in and on your own body and can enter into food in the work-place if you do not maintain high standards of personal hygiene.

HANDS

One of the easiest ways for bacteria to spread through the food area is from YOUR hands.

More than any other part of your body, your hands come into direct contact with food. Your hands also touch and can contaminate work-surfaces, trays, crockery and catering utensils which in turn may transfer the bacteria to food.

Thus it is important to **always wash your hands thoroughly** using hot water and soap (preferably liquid soap). Wash all parts of your hands and wrists under warm running water. And it is just as important to dry your hands thoroughly using a hot-air dryer or disposable paper towel.

The times when you must wash your hands are:

■ before entering the food area and before touching any food

■ after handling raw meat, poultry, shellfish, eggs or vegetables

■ after using the lavatory

■ after coughing into your hands or using a handkerchief

■ after touching your face or hair

■ after handling rubbish or cleaning

Bacteria can collect under finger-nails. Use a clean, nylon-bristled nail brush to clean them. Nail varnish may flake off and contaminate food.

It is important that you;

■ keep nails short and clean and do not wear nail varnish

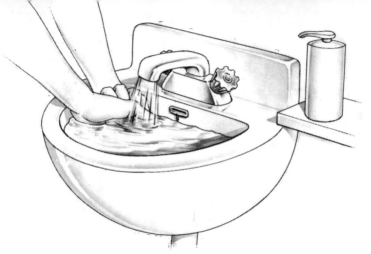

ALWAYS WASH YOUR HANDS
BEFORE HANDLING FOOD

**AFTER USING
THE TOILET**

**AFTER HANDLING
RAW FOODS**

AFTER CLEANING

FACE AND HEAD

Bacteria live in your nose, mouth, throat and ears and can be transferred by you to food, work-surfaces and equipment.

Bacteria also live in your hair and on your scalp. Unwashed hair carries more bacteria. Bacteria from your hair can easily fall into food.

You should:

Someone you know?

- avoid coughing or sneezing in a food room

- avoid touching your face and head— particularly your mouth, nose and ears

- keep your hair covered with a net or a hat

- shampoo your hair frequently

- NEVER comb your hair in a food area or while wearing protective clothing

6

JEWELLERY

It isn't a good idea to wear jewellery in a food area. Bacteria and food can gather on items such as rings and bracelets. The area of skin underneath the jewellery warms up thus further encouraging the growth of bacteria. Similar comments apply to watches: if you must wear one, remove it before washing your hands so that the wrists and forearms also can be washed.

Earrings, brooches and gemstones may fall into food.

The advice is:

- do not wear jewellery at work (an exception can be made for a plain ring)

WOUNDS

Wounds—cuts, grazes, scratches and boils—can quickly become infected with germs. The best way to prevent them from spreading to the food you handle is to make sure that all such wounds are properly covered.

You must:

■ keep all wounds covered by coloured waterproof dressings

■ tell your supervisor you are wearing a dressing: you may not be allowed to handle food

PROTECTIVE CLOTHING

Your everyday clothes can bring bacteria into the food area. The purpose of protective over-clothing or kitchen uniform is to prevent contamination from this source. But you can also spread bacteria if the over-clothing or uniform is soiled.

The rules are:

■ wear clean protective clothing at all times

■ do not wear your protective clothing away from work

NO SMOKING

You must not smoke in a food area—it is **against the LAW**.

6

Your hands can pick up bacteria either from your mouth or from the cigarette end. Bacteria can be transferred to a work-surface when you lay down your cigarette. Cigarette ash can fall into food.

REPORTING ILLNESS

Should you feel unwell or be suffering from a stomach disorder, cold or cough, or from an eye or ear discharge, report it to your supervisor. Report also if someone where you live seems to be suffering from a stomach bug.

Your employer may require other illnesses also to be reported.

If you visit a doctor with any of these complaints, tell him you are a food handler.

PEST CONTROL

This Section tells you about pests, the preventive action that you can take and the need to seek expert help.

PESTS AND FOOD

Three kinds of pests are commonly found in places where food for human consumption is prepared or stored:

- RODENTS—such as mice and rats
- INSECTS—such as houseflies, cockroaches, ants and a variety of other insects associated with food
- BIRDS—such as wild pigeons, magpies and sparrows

These pests eat and spoil food. They also transfer to the food the food poisoning bacteria they carry on their bodies and in their excreta.

PREVENTING ACCESS

Pests seek food, warmth and shelter. Take steps to keep them out.

You should:

- keep doors and windows closed so far as is practicable
- use fly screens on windows
- check deliveries for pests
- find the ways by which pests gain access
- do not do anything to attract pests to the premises, for example, by leaving kitchen waste uncovered in the outside bin

DENYING PESTS FAVOURABLE CONDITIONS

You can never be sure that pests will be kept out. But you can limit the pests' opportunities for contaminating food and the workplace.

To do this, adopt the following good working practices:

- promptly remove food particles and spillages from work-surfaces and floors

- do not leave utensils and equipment lying around uncleaned
- maintain a high standard of general cleaning
- cover any food that requires to ''stand out''
- do not leave food out overnight
- store dried foods in tightly lidded receptacles (this will also prevent moisture entering the food)
- regularly check all food storage areas
- empty waste receptacles regularly throughout the day and, for certain, at daily close of work

COMMON PESTS

RATS AND MICE

Mice can enter premises through a hole no larger than the diameter of a pencil and young rats through one not much bigger.

Once established within premises these pests are difficult to eradicate because of their high rate of breeding and resistance to chemical poisons called rodenticides. They will make nests in or near food premises using old packaging and food refuse.

Rats and mice carry bacteria on their fur and feet, and in their droppings and urine. They contaminate and spoil food in addition to eating it. In particular, they will attack stored food and this is one reason why you must frequently check and clean storage areas.

Usually, removal of rodents requires specialist treatment but the food handler can play a major role in ensuring that they are not attracted to the premises in the first place. High standards of cleanliness and food protection make life less easy for them.

HOUSEFLIES

Houseflies usually enter food premises through open doors, open windows and ventilators.

The pests breed from May to September anywhere there is de-composing food, faecal matter or general refuse.

Just as they will breed *anywhere*, houseflies will feed *anywhere* and may have enjoyed a meal in a sewer minutes before settling on a cream cake in your servery. A housefly will vomit and defecate on

the food it is eating and its legs and body will further contaminate the food. Then it will depart—usually unseen. If you needed only one reason for covering food at all times the housefly would provide it!

Flyscreens on windows and self-closing doors help to keep out flies and other insects. Sticky fly papers can be of use but require careful positioning, frequent renewal and careful disposal. Do not use insecticides in a food area unless under expert guidance.

The electronic insect killer—you may have seen this ultra-violet tube lighting equipment—lures and then kills insects that make contact. The dead insects fall into a tray. The wall-mounted equipment must be expertly sited well away from a light source and from any part of the food area where open food is dealt with. Frequent, careful, clearing of the tray is necessary.

COCKROACHES

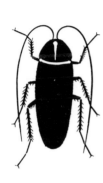

These pests are difficult to spot. Cockroaches live behind woodwork and in drains and other inaccessible places. They may be brought into premises with incoming food supplies so always check these carefully. Cockroaches come out at night.

Removing an infestation of cockroaches is a specialist task requiring the use of dangerous chemicals, but the food handler can play a preventive rôle by keeping clean all surfaces, floors and walls, and by generally avoiding a build-up of grease or food residues. Refuse receptacles must be thoroughly cleaned otherwise the cockroaches will breed in them.

BIRDS

Birds gain access through doors or windows and ventilator openings. Many commonly found birds scavenge for domestic food and contaminate food supplies through contact with their bodies, beaks or from their excreta.

Milk left outside premises is a common target. Throw away milk where there has been penetration of the carton or bottle-top.

Once established, birds are difficult to get rid of and this increases the importance of preventive measures. Outside waste receptacles must be lidded, with no refuse lying around. Birds thrive in the vicinity of take-away food shops and open-air eating places unless you ensure that uneaten food is binned promptly and the area is kept especially clean.

Professional pest controllers use nets and baits to trap birds and employ various techniques to deny them perches.

Cats, kittens, dogs, puppies and cage birds carry food poisoning bacteria and in the wrong place—the food area for instance—pets can become pests.

SPOTTING PESTS

Always look for the following *signs:*

- ■ droppings
- ■ marks on foods
- ■ small mounds of food debris
- ■ nibbled wrappings, holes in cardboard containers or pecked milk tops
- ■ pest carcasses
- ■ unusual smells
- ■ damage to woodwork—mice and rats gnaw

The food handler starting work early in the morning should be particularly vigilant in looking for the tell-tale signs—many pests do their work at night.

7

GET RID OF ANY FOOD THAT YOU SUSPECT MAY HAVE BEEN CONTAMINATED BY PESTS

GETTING RID OF PESTS

If you find signs of pests or suspect that the work-place is infested you must immediately tell your supervisor. Expert advice can be obtained from the Environmental Health Department of the local authority or from specialist private contractors.

The main steps that can be taken are:

- ● trapping and catching pests such as rodents and insects

  Many kinds of traps are available but knowledge of the habits of the pest is needed for complete success. NEVER use cats or dogs as "trappers": they are likely to spread bacteria themselves.

- laying poisons or other chemical substances

Poisoned baits, powders, etc. may be used but only where authorised and under expert supervision. Special cleaning of floors and surfaces may be necessary after such operations.

Poisons and chemicals must be handled with great care, kept away from food and be stored in a secure place.

7

KITCHEN DESIGN AND LAYOUT

This Section describes the standard of work-place that you should expect.

THE HYGIENIC KITCHEN

The design and layout of your kitchen can affect the standard of food hygiene that you can achieve.

A hygienic kitchen layout is one that allows plenty of space for work and storage, and provides separate working areas for each of the food categories—raw, high risk, vegetables and other. A key objective is to separate **"clean"** from **"dirty"** areas of operation.

The design and layout should assist cleaning and work-flow.

WORK-SURFACES

As work-surfaces are constantly in use, they must be strong, durable, and easily cleaned. Stainless steel tables with hollow steel legs are ideal. Braked castors on the base of work-surfaces and other items of equipment allow the items to be moved out of the way when the floor or walls are being cleaned.

FLOORS

A kitchen floor must be durable, easy to clean, non-absorbent, and non-slip. It should be resistant to acids, fat and grease.

The floor should be free of crevices and be coved at the angle with the wall. This will prevent food particles, dirt and grease—all of which can carry bacteria—from accumulating in areas where they are difficult to remove.

WALLS

Walls should be smooth and free from cracks and crevices—smooth plaster provides a suitable surface— with glazed tiles being used in those areas where the walls are likely to be splashed, such as behind sinks and above work-surfaces. Walls should be painted a light colour to show up dirt or grease.

CEILINGS

Ceilings should be smooth, light in colour and coved where they meet the walls.

VENTILATION

An effective system of ventilation is essential to remove the heat, steam, condensation and cooking odours of the kitchen — and to provide proper working conditions for the staff. A stuffy, moist room helps bacteria to grow.

LIGHTING

Kitchens must be well lit by natural or artificial lighting. Poor lighting makes it difficult to prepare food hygienically and to clean properly — and makes accidents more likely.

SINKS

Sinks should be provided for the washing of food. It will also be necessary to have a sink available for any hand-washing of dishes and utensils that may be required. Sinks should provide hot and cold water and preferably be of stainless steel.

WASTE DISPOSAL

Waste food can be disposed of efficiently and immediately using a waste disposal machine that breaks down the food before flushing it away through a waste pipe.

Waste food not disposed of in this way and general refuse should be placed in durable plastic bags and placed in bins reserved for this purpose. The bins should not be sited near food preparation areas.

8

TOILETS AND WASHING FACILITIES

Toilets must not lead directly on to food rooms.

Toilets should be well ventilated and have a sufficient number of wash-hand basins with roll towel or paper towel dispensers or hot-air dryers. Wrist operated taps reduce the risk of contamination from the hands.

Hand washing is less likely to be overlooked if the wash-hand basins are situated near the exit. A "NOW WASH YOUR HANDS" notice should be posted nearby.

There should be at least one wash-hand basin in the kitchen but this should be situated away from food preparation areas.

Wash-hand basins should have hot and cold running water and be suppled with liquid soap and nylon-bristle nail brushes.

WORK FLOW

Organising the kitchen into separate areas for separate jobs lies at the heart of hygienic kitchen design. The exact layout will depend upon the size of the kitchen as well as on the type of meals it prepares, but work must flow smoothly:

DELIVERY > STORAGE > PREPARATION >SERVICE

Storage rooms, refrigerators and freezers should be near delivery areas.

Vegetables and fruit should be prepared near their place of storage, away from other preparation areas to prevent the spread of soil.

Raw meat and poultry must not be dealt with near other foods.

Organising the kitchen in this way reduces the risk of raw food coming near cooked food, or of waste food or refuse contaminating food preparation areas.

WOOD

Avoid using wood in the kitchen. Wood wears quickly, is absorbent and can develop cracks and crevices in which bacteria can lodge. It is therefore unsuitable for use as floors, work-surfaces or as items of equipment such as chopping boards.

EXAMPLE OF THE LAYOUT OF A HYGIENIC CATERING KITCHEN

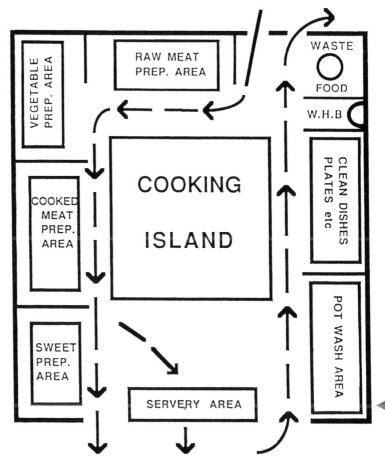

SEPARATION OF 'CLEAN' and 'DIRTY' AREAS

TEMPERATURE CONTROL

This Section specifies the action needed to avoid mistakes in the temperature control of food — the most common cause of problems.

TEMPERATURE AND BACTERIA

Bacteria will grow rapidly in foods, particularly in high risk foods, that are left *within* the Temperature Danger Zone — 5°C-63°C.

Bacteria do not grow, or grow only very slowly, at temperatures *below* 5°C.

They do not grow at temperatures *above* 63°C.

The idea behind correct temperature control is to keep food — above all the high risk foods — out of the Temperature Danger Zone. The rules for achieving this are quite simple:

■ keep hot food hot

■ keep cold food cold

■ keep prepared food out of the Temperature Danger Zone

Correct temperature control is a most powerful weapon against the infection of food by food poisoning bacteria.

This view is supported by research. A study of outbreaks of food poisoning occurring over a 12 year period found that most were caused by errors in temperature control.

9

COOKING FOOD

Bacteria are killed by heat. This is why food must be cooked thoroughly — most bacteria will not survive in food that is cooked at a temperature of *at least 70°C.* This temperature must be reached *throughout* the food *including the centre* and be held for *sufficient time.*

However, some bacterial spores and some bacterial poisons (toxins) are destroyed only if subjected to higher temperatures for a greater length of time.

MEAT AND POULTRY

All meat and poultry—particularly the latter—must be **thoroughly** cooked because of the likelihood of bacterial contamination.

The larger the joint of meat or poultry carcass, the longer it will take for the heat to reach the centre. If the cooking is not at a high enough temperature and for long enough, the centre may not be heated sufficiently to kill the bacteria. However, just enough warmth may reach the centre of the food to keep it *within* the Temperature Danger Zone so enabling food poisoning bacteria to grow rapidly.

The need for sufficiently high temperatures reaching the *centre* of the food must be kept in mind at all times. It is particularly important when cooking:

■ large joints of meat

   Large, thick joints should be cut into smaller pieces for cooking so that heat sufficient to destroy bacteria will reach the centre of each piece much more quickly.

■ rolled meat joints and beefburgers

   When present in meat, bacteria are usually on the surface and thus are easily killed by cooking heat. However, in a rolled joint or beefburger, bacteria that were on the surface become distributed throughout the food and it becomes more difficult for the heat to reach them.

■ poultry—particularly large carcasses

   Poultry can carry large numbers of bacteria and these are spread through the entire carcass. Cooking must ensure that the carcass is sufficiently heated to kill the bacteria wherever they may be.

   When a carcass is large, it is bad practice to cook the bird with the stuffing inside. The highest load of bacteria are inside where the intestines were. The stuffing can prevent heat sufficient to kill the bacteria reaching the centre of the bird. It is better to cook the bird and the stuffing separately.

9

SOUPS AND STOCK

It is bad practice to add a freshly made batch of soup or stock to a quantity made earlier but only partly used. "Topping up" is dangerous particularly when it continues over several services. During this time there will almost certainly be occasions when the temperature of the 'ever-on-the-go' pot will drop below the 63°C required for safety. Then the bacteria will multiply rapidly in the rich, warm, liquid food.

It is much safer if you:

■ prepare soups and stock in small quantities and discard anything left over at the end of the day

EGGS

Salmonella has been found *inside* a small percentage of eggs. As a safeguard, eggs should be cooked for around 7 minutes and to a temperature of 70°C. Avoid recipes based on uncooked or lightly cooked eggs: mayonnaise, mousses and certain sweets are examples of such dishes. Use recipes where pasteurised powdered or liquid eggs can be substituted.

KEEPING HOT FOODS HOT

High risk foods eaten immediately following cooking are safe providing the cooking temperature has been sufficiently high.

If, however, a short period will elapse between the time the food is ready and the time it will be eaten it is necessary to use equipment that will **hold** the food at a temperature of **63°C or above.** Heated trolleys and cupboards and heated food service counters are examples of such equipment.

Key points in their use are:

■ heat the *equipment* to at least 63°C before food is loaded

■ ensure that the *food* is already fully cooked and at a temperature of at least 63°C at the time of loading

■ NEVER use the *equipment* to heat up cold or partially heated food

KEEPING COLD FOODS COLD

9

Many foods that are eaten cold have sufficient nutrients and moisture to enable bacteria to grow quickly. Cold meats and poultry, prepared salads, pâtés, soft cheeses, sweets and cream are examples.

The rules for foods that will be eaten cold are:

■ keep under refrigeration until as near as possible to the time of consumption

■ handle as little as possible

■ keep away from other foods—particularly raw foods—and keep covered

KEEPING PREPARED FOOD OUT OF THE TEMPERATURE DANGER ZONE

If food is not to be served within a very short time of its being cooked it should be cooled to **under 10°C inside 90 minutes** of the end of cooking. It must be refrigerated immediately cooling is complete.

Quick cooling is important. In dropping back from its high cooking temperature to the cooled state the food will pass through the Temperature Danger Zone. It must spend as short a period as possible in the "Zone" because bacteria may have survived the cooking process and will mulitiply if given time.

Rapid cooling will be aided:

- by dividing food into smaller portions
- by the cooked foods being transferred to a cold receptacle that is then immersed in ice-cold water
- by the food being placed in the coolest part of the workplace (providing this does not carry the risk of cross-contamination)

RE-HEATING OF COOKED FOODS

Re-heated cooked foods—notably poultry and meat—are implicated in many cases of food poisoning. Food handlers often make the mistake of thinking that because food has already been cooked it is free of bacteria and that a "warming up" will be sufficient.

In fact, some bacteria—particularly in spore form—may not have been killed by the cooking. Or, following cooking, the food may have become contaminated by a food handler's hands or through cross-contamination.

If food contaminated by one of these means is *only lightly warmed*—instead of being thoroughly re-heated—bacteria will have ideal conditions for growth.

Observe these guidelines for food that is to be re-heated:

- do not remove the food from the refrigerator too far in advance of re-heating commencing
- handle the food as little as possible and keep it covered and clear of other foods
- divide large items into smaller portions
- heat the food to at least 70°C at its core

9

- serve quickly following re-heating
- NEVER re-heat cooked food more than once

  NOTE: If re-heating a ready-made cooked meal such as may be purchased in a super-market follow the manufacturer's instruc-tions in addition to the advice given above

REFRIGERATION

A refrigerator should operate at between 1°C and 4°C.

Placing food in a refrigerator does not kill the bacteria that the food may be carrying but the low temperature means that *warmth*—one of the require-ments for bacterial growth—is not present. The bacteria simply become dormant. If the food is removed from the refrigerator into room temperature the bacteria will begin to grow again.

Foods should be refrigerated for only short periods of time, the duration varying from food to food. Most foods fall within the 1-5 days' range but a few can be refrigerated for longer. Package labels often stipulate the maximum period of refrigeration. Food should not be refrigerated beyond its "use-by" date.

EXAMPLES OF REFRIGERATED STORAGE PERIODS

FOOD	DAYS	FOOD	DAYS
UNCOOKED MEATS		**COOKED MEATS**	
Poultry	2	Joint	3
Joint	3	Sliced	2
Minced	1	Pies	2
Sausages	3	Gravy	2
DAIRY		**FRUIT & VEGETABLES**	
Milk	4	Soft fruit	2
Cheese (soft)	2	Salad vegetables	5
Cheese (hard)	10	Greens	5

9

You should always refrigerate high risk foods and raw meat, poultry, eggs and seafood.

Points to remember about refrigeration:

- keep raw meat and poultry away from other foods—especially cooked meat and cooked poultry

- make sure that nothing—particularly raw meat and poultry—can drip on to food below

■ NEVER place cooked food in the refrigerator immediately after cooking: allow it to cool first

■ keep all food covered as far as possible

■ do not crowd food into the refrigerator—leave enough room for cold air to circulate

■ check at least **daily** that the temperature of the refrigerator is between 1°C and 4°C. *(See Record Chart below)*

■ open refrigerator doors as infrequently as possible and close them quickly

■ defrost the refrigerator regularly to prevent the build-up of ice. Keep it clean

TEMPERATURE RECORD CHART

Raw Meat Refrigerator No. ....
Temperature range 1°C-4°C

Date	Time	°C	Comments	Signature

FREEZING

Freezers keep food at a temperature (−22°C) well below freezing point. Freezing denies bacteria the warmth they need to grow. The coldness also turns any moisture in the food into ice—water in a form that bacteria cannot use.

Some bacteria will die as a result of freezing but others will survive although unable to grow. However, surviving bacteria will grow if the temperature rises towards the Temperature Danger Zone.

The length of time food can be stored in a frozen state depends on the type of food and the rating of the freezing unit. Although frozen food may not become contaminated it may deteriorate in flavour and character if stored too long. Different foods have different storage times ranging from 2 to 12 months. Check with the supplier of the food if you do not know how long it can remain frozen.

Points to remember about freezing:

- the freezer should lower the temperature of the food to −22°C. The temperature of the freezer must not rise above −18°C. Check **daily**

- wrap, label and date all food

- store food neatly within the freezer and do not overload

- use old stock before new—know the maximum storage periods

THAWING FOOD

Small items of food such as thin chops, fish cutlets and vegetables can be taken from the freezer and cooked direct without first being thawed.

But you cannot do this with **poultry, joints of meat and bulky items of food.** These foods MUST be completely thawed before cooking begins. Unless complete thawing occurs, the temperature at the core of the food may not reach a high enough level during the cooking process to kill any bacteria that are present.

Food has been completely thawed once it is soft and there are no ice crystals present. The legs of properly thawed poultry can be moved quite easily.

Thawing can cause problems in that when the

9

outer surface of the food warms up, bacteria can begin to grow although the centre of the food remains frozen.

THAWING METHODS—RAW MEAT AND POULTRY

For small meat joints and chickens, thawing can be carried out in a container in the refrigerator—on the bottom shelf.

The method of thawing large birds or joints of meat can give rise to difficulty. Thawing in the ordinary domestic refrigerator is not recommended because of the time this takes and the risk of other foods becoming contaminated. Microwave ovens can sometimes be used but they are not entirely satisfactory because the frozen food may thaw unevenly.

Where possible, large items should be allowed to thaw in air in a cool place (15°C or below). Special thawing cabinets are also available.

The time required to thaw meat or poultry depends upon the size of the piece and the temperature at which thawing is taking place.

GUIDANCE ON THAWING TIMES

	REFRIGERATOR	COOL ROOM
POULTRY		
1½ Kg (3.3 lb)	24 hrs	10 hrs
4 Kg (8.8 lb)	60 hrs	20 hrs
MEAT JOINTS		
1 Kg (2.2 lb)	8 hrs	4 hrs
3 Kg (6.6 lb)	42 hrs	16 hrs

When thawing raw meat and poultry:

- plan well ahead: know where you will be thawing and allow sufficient time for the operation

- place the frozen meat or poultry in a container to catch any liquid that drains off

- cover the thawing food

- keep the thawing food away from other foods, utensils and work-surfaces

- following thawing, cook the food immediately

- once frozen food has been thawed, NEVER RE-FREEZE IT

9

MEASUREMENT OF TEMPERATURE

The food handler should be able to measure temperatures, for example, those reached at the centre of foods during cooking or within a refrigerator.

Probe thermometers can be inserted into foods with the temperature result indicated by a dial or digital display. However, probes can pick up bacteria and should be cleaned both before and after use using an "alcohol wipe" disinfectant.

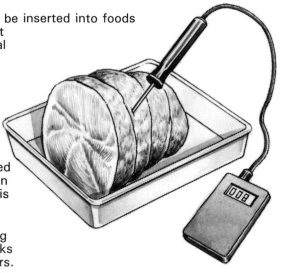

To measure the temperature *within* a refrigerator use a thermometer designed for this purpose. Place it on the top shelf. Normally, this is the warmest part of the interior.

Make a practice of taking frequent temperature checks on refrigerators and freezers. And keep a record of them.

COOK-CHILL AND COOK-FREEZE

COOK-CHILL is a system of food preparation that involves just what the name suggests. Immediately following thorough cooking, the food is rapidly *chilled* and then stored at a low temperature. Refrigerators and freezers are NOT suitable for chilling. Only purpose-built chilling equipment, known as a blast-chiller, should be used. Once chilled, the food is transferred to a refrigerated store reserved for cook-chill food and capable of maintaining the food at between 1°C and 3°C.

Cook-chill food can be stored under refrigeration for a maximum of 5 days *including* the day of production and the day of consumption. A cook-chill product carries a "Use by" date-mark based on this maximum safe life and this must be strictly observed.

Chilled food that rises above 10°C during storage must be discarded. If the temperature has risen above 5°C but not above 10°C the food must be eaten within 12 hours.

Food must be taken from the chill no more than 30 minutes prior to re-heating commencing or to the food being eaten cold.

Where cook-chill food is to be eaten hot, the re-heating should take place IMMEDIATELY BEFORE the food is due to be eaten. Food must be heated to a temperature of at least 70°C throughout and all preparation instructions followed — the larger the portion to be re-heated, the longer the re-heating time.

During service, the temperature of the food should not drop below 63°C.

COOK-FREEZE has many similarities to cook-chill but in this system, following cooking, the food is rapidly *frozen* and then stored in freezers where it can remain for between 2 and 12 months depending on the particular food. The rules for re-heating and serving applicable to cook-chill foods apply equally to cook-freeze items.

Producing food by cook-chill and cook-freeze methods requires special equipment and rigorous working practices to ensure strict control of temperature and very high standards of hygiene.

MICROWAVE OVENS

Microwave ovens use electromagnetic energy (microwaves) to heat and defrost food.

There are domestic (home) and commercial (catering) models of microwave ovens. Commercial models are more powerful electrically and are constructed to stand up to more intensive use. Domestic models are unsuitable for commercial use.

Most of the rules governing food preparation by conventional ovens apply also to microwave ovens. The cardinal rule remains that food that is being cooked or re-heated must reach at least 70°C at the core and hold this temperature long enough to destroy any bacteria present.

With microwave cooking some parts of the food may receive a concentration of waves and become very hot. Other parts may receive a less intensive barrage and be heated to a much lower temperature. These ''cold'' spots may result in bacteria not being destroyed.

To avoid food having ''hot'' and ''cold'' spots some ovens are fitted with a turntable so that all of the food can receive an equal application of heat. Always check that the food is piping hot throughout; if necessary, move the food around the oven or, if a liquid, stir to ensure adequate heating.

9

Immediately an oven is switched off microwave production stops and no more heat is received by the food. But the cooking process is not complete: the heat already within the food must be allowed time to spread throughout the food. Therefore always allow sufficient "standing time" after the oven has been switched off. Different foods require different standing times.

DRY FOOD STORAGE

All dry foods, such as flour, rice and pulses and all canned food, should be stored in a room or cupboard that is **cool, dry, clean** and **ventilated.**

Deliveries must be checked to ensure that goods that will be stored are free from odours, dampness or other form of soiling and do not harbour pests.

Food should be stored on shelves—no food on floor level—to reduce the risk of contamination by pests and to make the floor more accessible for cleaning.

"First in—first out" is one of the "golden rules" of stock control. Stock should be rotated so that the oldest food is used first. Identifying the order of use will be easier if stocks are date-labelled and are not crowded together on the shelves.

It is important to keep food covered at all times. Food that is not pre-packed, such as rice, should be stored in bins with tight fitting lids.

Most canned foods will keep for anything up to 3 years but for a few items—including canned fruit— the storage period is shorter if the food is to be eaten in prime condition. Poisoning from canned food is rare. Nevertheless, throw away—without opening them—any cans that are rusty, dented, or "blown" at the ends.

9

CLEANING AND DISINFECTION

**This Section describes some of the methods
available for cleaning and disinfecting utensils and
the work-place.**

CLEANING THE WORK-PLACE

Cleaning should achieve two things:

- the removal of grease, food debris and dirt
  generally
- the destruction of bacteria (disinfection)

Cleaning of the work-place can be divided into two
broad categories:

> *"clean-as-you-go"*   *"scheduled cleaning"*

CLEAN-AS-YOU-GO applies to cleaning that must
be done very quickly after the soiling occurs. The
aim is to prevent cross-contamination, or injury to
staff, or simply to keep working areas clean and
tidy.

Examples of this type of cleaning are:

- washing and sanitising of a chopping board
  immediately after use
- cleaning up of a floor spillage just after it has
  happened

10

SCHEDULED CLEANING refers to cleaning operations carried out at specified intervals. The duration of these intervals varies from item to item: a floor in a kitchen requires to be cleaned more frequently than the shelves in a store room.

Examples of this type of cleaning are:

● Scrub, rinse and dry kitchen floor to leave clear of all grease, dirt and food residues—DAILY at close of work.

● Clean all shelves and ledges in dry store— WEEKLY (Tuesday)

The key to effective cleaning is to decide for each cleaning operation:

■ whether it should be *"clean-as-you-go"* or *"scheduled"*

■ the method of cleaning, the cleaning materials and equipment (if any) to be used

■ the precautions to be taken, e.g. wearing of rubber gloves

■ who will do the cleaning

■ where *"scheduled"*, the frequency of cleaning

Do not make the mistake of using *"scheduled cleaning"* for items that should be dealt with immediately under *"clean-as-you-go"*.

CLEANING AND DISINFECTION CHEMICALS

Chemicals are available to enable you to maintain proper standards of cleaning and disinfection. Usually the chemical is added to water to make the cleaning solution.

DETERGENTS are chemicals that will dissolve grease and assist the removal of food debris and dirt. Detergents do not kill bacteria.

DISINFECTANTS are chemicals designed to destroy bacteria. They reduce the number of bacteria to a safe level. Disinfectants are not effective in removing dirt and grease. Some have a strong smell and may leave chemical traces. The need to use them in the work-place is very limited.

SANITIZERS are chemicals combining the role of both detergent and disinfectant. They are designed to remove grease and dirt AND to disinfect in one operation.

Disinfection by HEAT—for example, using really hot water—is a most effective way of killing off bacteria. Chemical disinfectants and sanitizers can be used in addition or in situations where hot water is not available. However they are less effective in water that is not hot and on surfaces that have not received a preliminary clean using hot water and a detergent.

It is a popular myth that the use of disinfectants achieves perfect hygiene. They are useful in reducing the numbers of bacteria on surfaces that come into contact with food, as well as for floors and toilet areas, but care must be taken to ensure that the food itself is not contaminated by the disinfectant.

When using cleaning solutions:

- ■ follow the "Instructions for Use" including those for dilution and storage
- ■ make up fresh, hot solutions frequently: dirty or cool water makes the chemicals less effective
- ■ wear rubber gloves or other protective clothing when necessary
- ■ do not store chemicals within the food area or where they may warm up
- ■ NEVER mix different chemicals—they become less effective when mixed and you may produce poisonous gases

DISH WASHING

Crockery, cutlery and utensils should be cleaned immediately after use. Cleaning can be by hand or by machine.

WASHING BY HAND

The most hygienic way to wash by hand is with TWO stainless-steel sinks side by side. Wash in one and rinse in the other.

If you do not have two sinks, you can clean and then rinse in the same sink or wash in the sink and rinse in a separate bowl of hot water.

Rinse water should be changed frequently, when dirty or cooled. Rinsing is important. Laboratory tests have shown that dishes that are not rinsed are covered with large numbers of bacteria.

Adopt the following steps when dish-washing:

1. wear rubber gloves
   This will protect your hands from scalding and the effects of detergents.
2. remove left-over food
   This can be done by scraping and rinsing under running water.
3. wash in hot water and detergent
   In the first sink, items are placed into hot water (50°C-60°C) and detergent, and scrubbed with a tough nylon-bristled brush.
4. rinse in very hot water
   In the second sink (or in the bowl) items are rinsed in very hot water (75°C-80°C) before being stacked to dry. As well as killing bacteria and removing detergent, rinsing in this way makes the items hot enough to dry quickly on contact with the air. This avoids the need for drying cloths which can spread bacteria if they become soiled.
5. dry
   After rinsing, the items should be left to drain in a clean, dry area, well away from any dirty washing water, until they are clean, dry and without smears.

WASHING BY MACHINE

There are several types of dish and utensil-washing machines available but they all follow the stages of cleaning just mentioned—left-over food is removed from the items to be washed which are then stacked in the machine. Washing is by very hot water and detergent followed by rinsing and disinfecting by hot water sprays or steam.

Correct loading of these machines is essential. Items should be stacked neatly so that the cleaning solution can reach them. Cups, glasses and jugs should be stacked upside-down to avoid collecting water.

The correct amount of detergent must be used.

Whichever kind of machine you use it will clean effectively only if the washing and rinsing occur at the correct temperatures. A machine that does not operate at the proper temperature is a hazard.

CLEANING WORK-SURFACES

It is vital that surfaces upon which food is prepared are kept clean and bacteria-free for each new job. *"Clean-as-you-go"* applies but there may also be a *"scheduled"* requirement to clean the surfaces at the daily start of work. Work-surfaces should be left clean and clear at close of work.

The stages of cleaning are:

1. remove food particles and spillages using a damp cloth
2. use a solution of detergent and very hot water to remove grease and general soiling
3. rinse the surface thoroughly using very hot water
4. apply a suitable sanitizer in very hot water; allow sufficient time for the solution to do its work
5. rinse again using very hot water and leave the surface to dry. Alternatively, dry the surface using disposable paper towels

If the soiling is very light you may be able to omit stages "2" and "3" but **do not do so** if the surface has been in contact with raw meat, poultry, shellfish or eggs.

CLEANING OTHER SURFACES

Telephones, and handles on doors and refrigerators, are examples of surfaces where contaminated hands may deposit bacteria which can be picked up by other hands. Include such surfaces in the cleaning schedule.

CLEANING EQUIPMENT

You should not attempt to clean equipment unless you have been trained and authorised to do so.

The basic steps are:

1. disconnect the machinery from any power source before commencing cleaning. Take extra care if removing blades
2. remove all waste food
3. thoroughly wash and sanitize all parts
4. re-assemble the machine taking particular care if there is a moving part that could fly off if not properly refitted
5. sanitize (again) those parts of the machine that will come into contact with food
6. ensure all guards have been refitted

CLEANING FLOORS, WALLS AND CEILINGS

FLOORS

Cleaning of floors can be by machine-scrubber or by manual scrubbing using hot water and detergent. Where a hand scrubber or mop is being used, work with two buckets, one holding the hot cleaning solution. The other bucket should hold plain hot water for removing dirty water and soil from the hand scrubber or mop-head as cleaning proceeds.

Following scrubbing, the floor should be rinsed using either a machine or a detachable-head mop. Very hot water aids quick drying.

Clean **all** areas of the floor paying particular attention to parts where food residues may have lodged.

Where cleaning is required during the day this can usually be done by mopping. Food spillages should be cleaned up as they occur.

A wet floor is a hazard to staff: during cleaning and drying a warning notice should be displayed.

It is important that a floor is left clean and free from food residues at the daily close of work. Dirty floors are an invitation to pests to take up residence.

WALLS AND CEILINGS

Most walls and ceilings can be satisfactorily cleaned using very hot water and a detergent or sanitizer. A disinfectant should be used daily for wall areas where splashes and stains may occur such as behind sinks or work-surfaces.

DUSTING AND SWEEPING

Dry dusting and sweeping can fill the air with dust particles that may well be carrying bacteria. Use a moist cloth—never a dry duster—for ledges and shelves. For floors, wrap a clean damp cloth around the brush head if no better alternative exists.

SCRUBBERS, MOPS AND CLOTHS

Scrubbers, mops and cloths become contaminated with bacteria during cleaning. They must be thoroughly washed and disinfected frequently. Mop heads and floor cloths should be boiled from time to time.

WASTE RECEPTACLES

Waste receptacles can become breeding grounds for insects and rodents, their contents providing the food and shelter these pests need.

WASTE BINS WITHIN THE FOOD AREA

Bins and bin stands must be washed down and disinfected regularly, the task being included in the cleaning schedule. The floor area around bins must be cleaned at least daily.

EXTERNAL WASTE BINS

"Outside" waste receptacles—bins and skips—should be positioned as far away from the food area as is practicable and should have lids or covers to limit access by pests.

Keep the area around the receptacles tidy: do not leave waste material stacked up *outside* the bin or skip. Hose down the area after each collection by the local authority. During the summer months it may be necessary to disinfect the receptacles or to spray them with insecticides.

10

CLEAN THOROUGHLY
CLEANING DONE BADLY SIMPLY SPREADS THE BACTERIA!

FOOD HYGIENE AND THE LAW

This Section picks out a few points of concern to you from the large amount of law concerning food hygiene.

THE LAW

There is a considerable amount of law designed to protect the public against food that is unfit to eat.

The Food Hygiene (General) Regulations 1970

The Regulations lay down minimum requirements for the maintenance and cleanliness of food premises and equipment; the hygienic handling of food; the personal cleanliness of food handlers and the washing facilities that should be available to them.

The Regulations contain definitions of ''food business'', ''food room'', ''premises'' and ''preparation''.

The Food Safety Act 1990

The Act is a most important piece of legislation covering the entire food chain from farmer through to food factories, restaurants, stalls, shops—really any businesses involved with food.

The intention of the Act is to protect the consumer against bad food or food that is misleadingly described and to eliminate unhygienic practices. The legislation gives local authorities stronger powers to enforce food laws and increases the penalties the Courts can impose if the law is broken. The Act enables Ministers to issue codes of recommended practice and a number of such Codes have already been issued. The Act also provides for the making of Regulations for the training of food handlers.

The Food Hygiene (Amendment) Regulations 1990

The Regulations set out the legal requirements for the temperature control of food.

The following paragraphs summarise those parts of food law that are of particular importance to the food handler.

PREVENTION OF CONTAMINATION OF FOOD BY FOOD HANDLERS

Food handlers must:

- avoid exposing food to the risk of contamination
- report if suffering from upset stomachs, colds or coughs
- keep cuts covered by a suitable waterproof dressing
- not smoke or spit in the food area
- keep themselves and their clothing clean and wear clean over-clothing when on duty

FOOD PREMISES

There is a general requirement that a food business must not be carried on in insanitary premises. Food premises must be:

- registered with the local authority
- maintained in good condition, kept clean and free from accumulation of waste and refuse
- adequately supplied with clean water
- well lit and well ventilated
- provided with hot/cold water sinks or other means for washing utensils, equipment and food
- supplied with toilets and wash-hand basins for the use of staff and have facilities for keeping their personal clothes
- equipped with first-aid materials

EQUIPMENT

All food equipment must be kept clean and in good working order.

WASHING AND TOILET FACILITIES

Wash-hand basins must have a supply of hot and cold water and be provided with soap, nail-brushes and clean towels or other means of drying. Wash-hand basins must be used for personal cleanliness only.

Toilets must be provided and be situated in a room separate from the food area.

11

Wash and toilet rooms must be kept clean and in good repair. They must be well lit, well ventilated and carry notices directing that employees wash their hands after using the toilet.

NOTE: There must be a rigid separation in use between (i) wash-hand basins—for personal cleanliness only and (ii) sinks—for washing of utensils, equipment and food only.

TEMPERATURE CONTROL OF FOOD

The Food Hygiene (Amendment) Regulations 1990 detail the temperatures at which specified foods must be kept. These are foods known to be particularly vulnerable to contamination by food poisoning bacteria. You have already met most of them when discussing high risk foods.

The purpose of the legislation is to ensure that the foods are kept *outside* the Temperature Danger Zone.

Foods listed in the Regulations must be held:

at **63°C** or above

OR

8°C or below

except for

certain foods where the maximum permitted lower temperature is:

5°C

NOTE

Most food poisoning bacteria will not grow much in food held at a temperature of 8°C.

But there are some harmful bacteria that can grow at temperatures lower than this. The Regulations identify the foods that are at risk and lay down the lower temperature limit of 5°C for the cold storage of such foods.

Throughout this book you have been advised to store ALL foods requiring refrigeration at 5°C or below. SAFETY FIRST

DATE-MARKING OF FOODS

Highly perishable foods must carry a "Use by" date-mark. It is an offence to sell food after this date. The food can be used up to and including the date shown.

Most other foods must carry a "Best before" (or "Best before end") date-mark, this indicating the date (or end of month) up until which the food will be in the best condition for eating.

11

Some foods are not required by law to bear a date-mark—fresh fruit, vegetables, butcher meat, are examples.

It is an offence for a date-mark to be changed other than by the person responsible for the original date-marking.

ENFORCING THE LAW

An authorised officer of a local authority has powers of entry to food premises and may require steps be taken to comply with the law. If the officer considers that there is an imminent risk to public health the officer may immediately close part or the whole of a business, but must also take the matter to Court.

Businesses may be taken to Court even when they have not been partly or wholly closed. Courts have powers to close parts or the whole of a business and can impose fines of up to £20,000 and prison sentences of up to six months. In extremely serious cases even higher fines and longer terms of imprisonment may be imposed.

A person accused of an offence under the Food Safety Act 1990 may plead that he had taken all *reasonable precautions* and exercised all *due diligence* to avoid the offence being committed by himself or by someone under his control.

In his defence a food trader may seek to prove that he had analysed all his operations, had identified areas where hygiene risks could arise and had introduced procedures to eliminate them. For example, he may be able to show that food bought in for re-sale is checked for contamination.

The trader's case may also be assisted if there are records of such operations as regular checks of food temperature, good freezer maintenance, and of staff being given training in food hygiene.

The defence of *due diligence* therefore provides a balance between (i) the right of the consumer to be protected against defective food and (ii) the right of traders not to be convicted of offences they have taken all reasonable care to avoid committing.

"WHAT SHOULD I DO?"

WASH YOUR HANDS

- before entering the food area
- after using the lavatory
- between handling raw meat/poultry/shellfish/eggs AND high-risk foods
- before and after touching food
- after coughing into your hands or using a handkerchief
- after touching your face or hair
- after carrying out any cleaning or handling of rubbish

Avoid touching your nose or coughing or sneezing over food

Avoid touching food with your hands. Whenever possible use tongs to handle food and plates or trays to carry it

---

Avoid touching those parts of dishes or cutlery that come into direct contact with food

---

Keep your hair covered with a net or disposable hat and do not comb hair in a food area

---

"WHY SHOULD I DO IT?"

There are many bacteria on the surface of your skin. Most are harmless but some, when transferred to food, can cause illness. In addition, your hands can pick up bacteria from other sources and contaminate food

Handling raw meat/poultry and then going on to handle cooked meat is particularly dangerous unless you wash your hands thoroughly in between

---

Personal cleanliness is vital, otherwise you add your own bacteria to the food

---

The less your hands are in direct contact with food, the less chance there is of contamination occurring

---

Bacteria on your hands may be transferred to food via the dish or the cutlery

---

Your hair and scalp carry many bacteria that can fall into food

---

"WHAT SHOULD I DO?"

Keep finger-nails short and clean and do not wear nail varnish

Avoid wearing hand/wrist jewellery, earrings, brooches or stoned rings

Keep cuts, grazes and boils covered with a waterproof dressing that is brightly coloured—blue is a good colour

Inform your supervisor if you have a stomach upset, boils, cough, cold, or eye or ear discharges. And also report if you have a sore or a wound even if it is covered by a waterproof dressing

Wear clean protective over-clothing

Do not smoke in a food area

Keep raw and cooked foods separate especially raw meat/poultry and cooked meat/poultry

"WHY SHOULD I DO IT?"

Bacteria can collect beneath long nails and pass into the food you handle. Varnish can enter food

Bacteria can collect on these items. Stones or metal may fall into food. Hand/wrist washing is more thorough.

Wounds such as these are often infected with bacteria. They must be properly covered to prevent the spread of bacteria. Coloured dressings will be easily spotted if they fall into food

If you are suffering from any of these conditions you may contaminate food

Your own clothing may carry bacteria

It's against the law and can lead to food becoming contaminated

Raw foods can spread bacteria to other foods that will be eaten without further cooking. Keep them apart both on work-surfaces and within the refrigerator

"WHAT SHOULD I DO?"	"WHY SHOULD I DO IT?"
Keep food at the correct temperature—in storage and preparation ● Remember the "High Risk" foods ● Remember the "Temperature Danger Zone"	High risk foods (e.g. meat, poultry, gravy etc.) provide bacteria with the nutrients and moisture needed to grow. In the Temperature Danger Zone (5°C to 63°C) bacteria multiply at a very fast rate
Cook food thoroughly so that the centre is heated to a temperature of at least 70°C for a sufficient length of time	This is necessary to kill bacteria —but even so, some may survive
Following cooking, cool food quickly and refrigerate it unless it is needed for current service	To limit the time the food spends in the Temperature Danger Zone
Avoid preparing food too far in advance or removing it from the refrigerator too early	To reduce the risk of food being held in the Temperature Danger Zone
Be sure that certain frozen food is thawed thoroughly before cooking —especially poultry and large joints of meat	Thorough thawing is essential if the centre of the food is to reach the temperature required to destroy bacteria during cooking
Never re-freeze raw food	Bacteria in the food will have multiplied during thawing. Re-freezing the raw food will lock in these bacteria and they will become very active when the raw food is thawed for a second time

"WHAT SHOULD I DO?"	"WHY SHOULD I DO IT?"
Keep food covered whenever possible	To protect it against contamination
Rotate food stocks and observe ''Use By'' and ''Best Before'' dates	Using food stocks in the correct order reduces the risk of bacteria multiplying and the quality of the food being affected
Always ensure that the workplace is clean before preparing food	Thorough cleaning is necessary to kill any bacteria already present
Clean kitchen utensils and equipment thoroughly, before and after use	Utensils and equipment may have become contaminated by bacteria
Use clean wiping cloths	Dirty cloths spread bacteria
Never mix different cleaning solutions	This can make the mixture ineffective and may also cause poisonous gases to be given off
''Clean as you go''. Any surfaces or equipment that have been in contact with raw food must be cleaned up there and then. So must spillages	To avoid the risk of cross-contamination
Compile a cleaning schedule for the entire work-place	You will have a list of ALL that must be done, how and by whom. And a timetable for doing it

MORE ABOUT BACTERIA

This Appendix provides additional information on some of the bacteria usually associated with food related-illnesses within the United Kingdom. The way in which bacterial growth can be affected by oxygen and acids is also briefly discussed.

KINDS OF BACTERIA

SALMONELLA bacteria are found in raw meat and poultry, in foods prepared from them and in eggs.

The risk of food poisoning from Salmonella infection of raw meat and raw poultry has been well known for many years. Poultry meat in particular is heavily infected.

The risk from eggs was thought to arise from Salmonella adhering to the outside of the shell being transferred to the inside when the shell was broken or accidentally cracked. This remains a danger but there is now also a risk from a new strain of Salmonella that is found *inside the egg* because the egg-laying apparatus of the hen has become infected.

All of the foods mentioned require thorough cooking and careful post-cooking handling (refrigeration, keeping covered, etc.) to prevent re-contamination. The bacteria are also found in the gut of humans and will be spread to food by a handler who has poor standards of toilet hygiene.

Salmonella bacteria are a **major** cause of food poisoning.

CLOSTRIDIUM PERFRINGENS is found in the gut of animals and humans. The organism is also found in soil. The bacteria produce spores which may not be killed during cooking or re-heating. Meat and poultry are frequently contaminated. Food that is not to be eaten immediately following cooking must be cooled rapidly then refrigerated to prevent the spores germinating.

The bacteria are a frequent cause of food poisoning.

STAPHYLOCOCCUS AUREUS lives in and on the human body — in the nose and mouth and in cuts and boils. The bacteria are relatively harmless so long as they stay on the human body. But they will multiply rapidly if transferred to foods. The bacteria produce a toxin (poison) that is difficult to destroy with heat.

The bacteria can be transferred to food if a food handler has inadequate standards of personal hygiene. Any food that is handled or left uncovered can be contaminated but cooked meats, sandwiches and products containing cream are most at risk.

The bacteria are implicated in fewer reported cases of food poisoning than either Salmonella or Clostridium perfringens.

BACILLUS CEREUS is particularly associated with rice but can be found in other cereal foods. The bacteria, usually in spore form, are dormant when the food is dry but become active when water is added at cooking. These spores may survive ordinary cooking temperatures.

If cooked or partly cooked rice is allowed to "stand out" at a warm temperature the bacteria will grow rapidly producing a toxin (poison) that is unlikely to be destroyed even by subsequent re-heating.

Only a small proportion of the total number of reported food poisoning cases have been attributed to the bacteria.

CAMPYLOBACTER JEJUNI is a major source of diarrhoea. Since the early 1980s the reported cases of campylobacter infections have exceeded those for Salmonella. Cattle, pigs, poultry, birds and pets carry the bacteria. The infection spreads to humans in much the same way as Salmonella, i.e. mainly from the bacteria being present in raw foods of animal origin with, once again, poultry being high on the list.

Other sources of infection have been identified. Water supplies have been implicated as has unpasteurised milk, and bottled milk which has been pecked by birds.

LISTERIA MONOCYTOGENES is found in the gut of animals and humans, in soil, in sewage and throughout the environment. The bacteria can be passed into the milk of infected animals. Most people have carried the bacteria in their gut at one time or another and for the vast majority it causes no harm when swallowed. But two groups of people have been identified as being at risk—a small group of people with weakened immunity and women who are pregnant.

The bacteria are unusual in that they can grow in the refrigerator—albeit slowly—at temperatures that are too cold for other bacteria to grow. Short period storage at a very low temperature is essential for foods associated with Listeria—pâtés, cooked chicken, prepared salads and soft cheeses.

Listeria can cause serious illness, but fortunately the number of reported cases is relatively small.

E.COLI. You may have read of outbreaks of illness due to E.coli 0157 as a result of people eating undercooked beefburgers.

The bacterium Escherichia coli is normally found in the bowels of people and animals and its presence is essential. Thus the germ is found anywhere where faecal contamination occurs—on the ground, in sewage, in water and in food often associated with poor personal hygiene.

Variants of the bacteria, E.coli 0157 is one, can in certain circumstances be harmful to humans, especially those who are vulnerable such as babies and young children.

BACTERIA AND OXYGEN

To grow, some bacteria require the presence of oxygen: these are classified as "aerobic". Others that will *not* grow if oxygen is present are classified as "anaerobic". There are also bacteria that can tolerate either condition.

Sometimes it is possible to deny bacteria the environment they favour. For example, the risk from aerobic-type bacteria can be reduced by vacuum packaging, i.e. the air is extracted from the wrapper containing the food.

BACTERIA AND ACIDS

Bacteria do not like acid and if enough is present in food they will not grow. The extent to which foods are acidic is measured on the "pH" scale.

A measurement of pH 7.0 denotes that a food is "neutral"; bacteria grow best in neutral foods.

Measurements lower than pH 7.0 indicate that acid is present; the lower the figure, the more acid there is in the food. Foods measuring pH 3.7 or lower are known as "high acid" foods. Bacteria do not find such foods suitable for their growth.

Chicken (pH 6.3) is an example of a near neutral food; grapefruit (pH 3.0) exemplifies the high acid foods that provide little scope for bacteria to grow.